CW00408200

Easy-to-Play
FAVOURITE
WORSHIP
SONGS

The top 24 songs easily arranged for keyboard
with guitar chords and complete texts.
Arranged by Christopher Tambling

Kevin
Mayhew

We hope you enjoy the music in this book. Further copies are available
from your local music shop or Christian bookshop.

In case of difficulty, please contact the publisher direct by writing to:

The Sales Department
KEVIN MAYHEW LTD
Rattlesden
Bury St Edmunds
Suffolk
IP30 0SZ

Phone 01449 737978
Fax 01449 737834

Please ask for our complete catalogue of outstanding Church Music.

First published in Great Britain in 1996 by Kevin Mayhew Ltd.

© Copyright 1996 Kevin Mayhew Ltd.

ISBN 0 86209 837 8
Catalogue No: 1450050

The texts and music in this book are protected by copyright and may not be reproduced
in any way for sale or private use without the consent of the copyright owner.

Front cover photograph courtesy of Pictor International, London.
Used by kind permission.
Cover design by Graham Johnstone and Veronica Ward.

Music arrangements by Christopher Tambling
Music Editor: Donald Thomson

Printed and bound in Great Britain

Contents

ALL HAIL THE LAMB

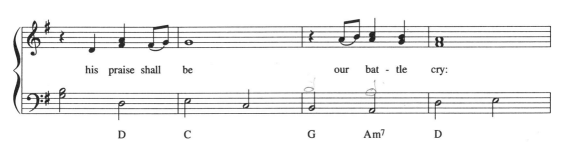

Words and music: Dave Bilbrough

Copyright © 1988 Kingsway's Thankyou Music, P.O. Box 75,
Eastbourne, East Sussex, BN23 6NW. Used by permission.

REJOICE!

Triumphantly

Refrain

Re - joice! re-joice! Christ is in you, the hope of glo - ry in our hearts. He

D   G   D   Bm(D)   Em   A

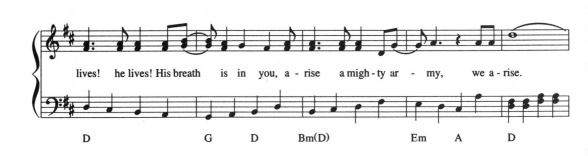

lives! he lives! His breath is in you, a - rise a migh-ty ar - my, we a - rise.

D   G   D   Bm(D)   Em   A   D

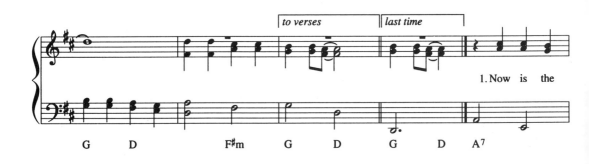

to verses | *last time*

1. Now is the

G   D   F#m   G   D   G   D   A⁷

time for us to march u - pon the land; in - to our hands he will give the ground we

Bm(D)   G   A⁷

Copyright © 1983 Kingsway's Thankyou Music, P.O. Box 75,
Eastbourne, East Sussex BN23 6NW. Used by permission.

claim. He rides in ma-jes-ty to lead us in-to

D   A⁷   Bm(D)

D.S.

vic-to-ry; the world shall see that Christ is Lord! Re-

G   Bm(D)   Em   A

2. God is at work in us
   his purpose to perform,
   building a kingdom
   of power, not of words,
   where things impossible,
   by faith, shall be made possible;
   let's give the glory
   to him now.

3. Though we are weak, his grace
   is everything we need;
   we're made of clay
   but this treasure is within.
   He turns our weaknesses
   into his opportunities,
   so that the glory
   goes to him.

Words and music: Graham Kendrick

I BELIEVE IN JESUS

With conviction

I be-lieve in Je - sus; I be-lieve he is the Son of God.

E A B E A B

I be-lieve he died and rose a-gain, I be-lieve he paid for us all.

E A B E A B

Women (2nd time) I be-lieve that you're here, *All*

Men And I be-lieve he's here now, stand-ing in our midst.

A B E A B E

Women With the po - wer to heal, *All*

Men Here with the po - wer to heal now, and the grace to for - give.

A B E A B E

2. I believe in you, Lord;
   I believe you are the Son of God.
   I believe you died and rose again,
   I believe you paid for us all.
   And I believe you're here now,
   standing in our midst.
   Here with the power to heal now,
   and the grace to forgive.

Words and music: Marc Nelson

Copyright © 1987 Mercy/Vineyard Publishing. Administered in the UK and Eire by Integrity's Hosanna! Music,
P.O. Box 101, Eastbourne, East Sussex BN21 4SZ. All rights reserved. International copyright secured.
Used by permission.

BE BOLD, BE STRONG

Words and music: Morris Chapman

Copyright © 1983 Word Music Inc./Word Music (UK). Administered by CopyCare Ltd,
P.O. Box 77, Hailsham, East Sussex BN27 3EF. Used by permission.

MEEKNESS AND MAJESTY

Majestically

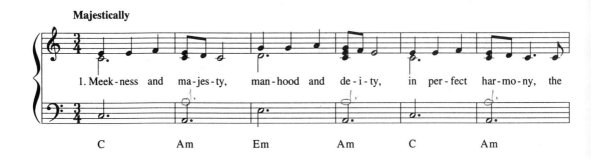

1. Meek-ness and ma-jes-ty, man-hood and de-i-ty, in per-fect har-mo-ny, the

C   Am   Em   Am   C   Am

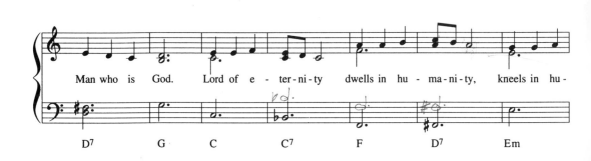

Man who is God. Lord of e-ter-ni-ty dwells in hu-ma-ni-ty, kneels in hu-

D7   G   C   C7   F   D7   Em

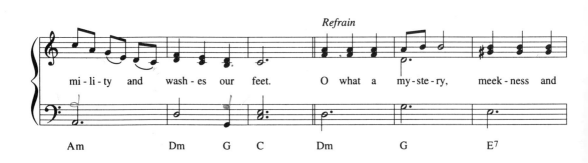

Refrain

mi-li-ty and wash-es our feet. O what a mys-te-ry, meek-ness and

Am   Dm   G   C   Dm   G   E7

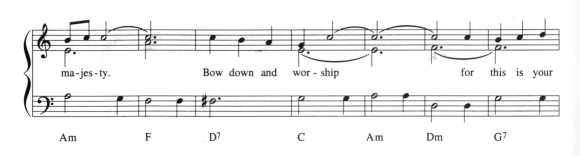

ma-jes-ty. Bow down and wor-ship for this is your

Am   F   D7   C   Am   Dm   G7

Copyright © 1986 Kingsway's Thankyou Music, P.O. Box 75,
Eastbourne, East Sussex BN23 6NW. Used by permission.

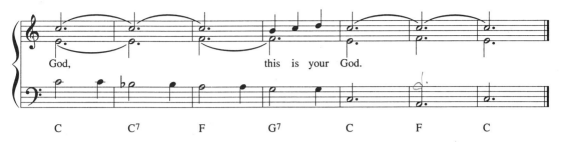

God,   this is your God.

C   C⁷   F   G⁷   C   F   C

2. Father's pure radiance,
   perfect in innocence,
   yet learns obedience
   to death on a cross.
   Suffering to give us life,
   conquering through sacrifice,
   and as they crucify
   prays: 'Father forgive.'

3. Wisdom unsearchable,
   God the invisible,
   love indestructable
   in frailty appears.
   Lord of infinity,
   stooping so tenderly,
   lifts our humanity
   to the heights of his throne.

Words and music: Graham Kendrick

YOU LAID ASIDE YOUR MAJESTY

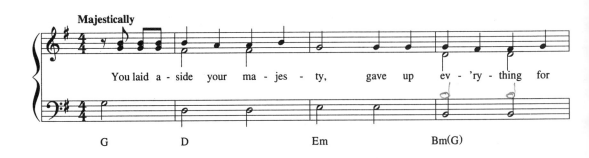

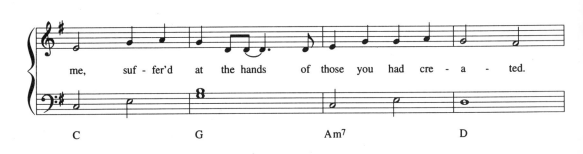

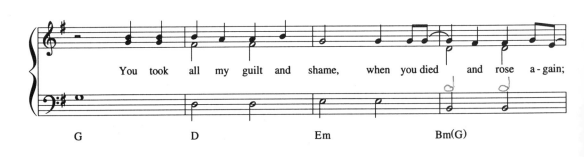

© Copyright 1985 Kingway's Thankyou Music, P.O. Box 75, Eastbourne, East Sussex, BN23 6NW. Used by permission.

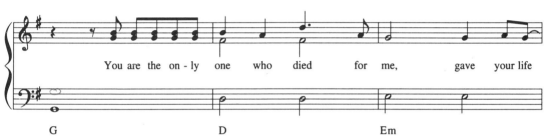

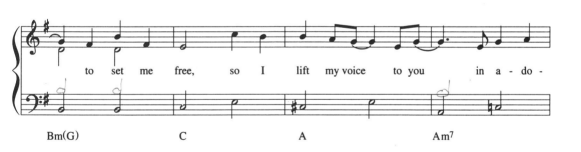

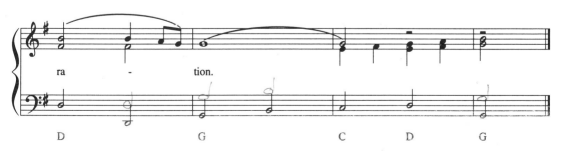

Words and music: Noel Richards

JESUS PUT THIS SONG INTO OUR HEARTS

2. Jesus taught us how to live in harmony,
   Jesus taught us how to live in harmony,
   different faces, different races, he made us one,
   Jesus taught us how to live in harmony.

3. Jesus taught us how to be a family,
   Jesus taught us how to be a family,
   loving one another with the love that he gives,
   Jesus taught us how to be a family.

4. Jesus turned our sorrow into dancing,
   Jesus turned our sorrow into dancing,
   changed our tears of sadness into rivers of joy,
   Jesus turned our sorrows into a dance.

5. *Instrumental*

Words and music: Graham Kendrick

Copyright © 1986 Kingsway's Thankyou Music, P.O. Box 75,
Eastbourne, East Sussex BN23 6NW. Used by permission.

PURIFY MY HEART

Refiner's Fire

Words and music: Brian Doerksen

Copyright © 1990 Mercy/Vineyard Publishing. Administered in the UK and Eire by Integrity's Hosanna! Music,
P.O. Box 101, Eastbourne, East Sussex BN21 4SZ. All rights reserved. International copyright secured.
Used by permission.

15

THERE IS POWER IN THE NAME OF JESUS

1. There is pow'r in the name of Je - sus; we be - lieve in his name. We have called on the name of Je - sus; we are saved! We are saved! At his name the de - mons flee.

Copyright © 1989 Kingsway's Thankyou Music, P.O. Box 75,
Eastbourne, East Sussex BN23 6NW. Used by permission.

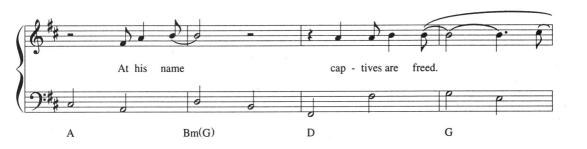

At his name cap - tives are freed.

A   Bm(G)   D   G

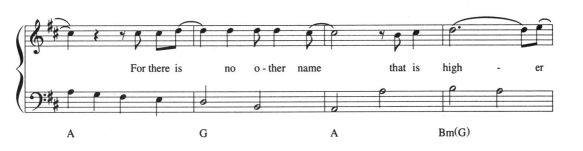

For there is no o - ther name that is high - er

A   G   A   Bm(G)

than Je - sus!

E   G   A⁷   D

2. There is power in the name of Jesus,
   like a sword in our hands.
   We declare in the name of Jesus;
   we shall stand! we shall stand!
   At his name God's enemies
   shall be crushed beneath our feet.
   For there is no other name that is higher
   than Jesus!

Words and music: Noel Richards

FROM HEAVEN YOU CAME

The Servant King

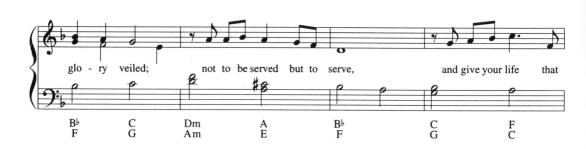

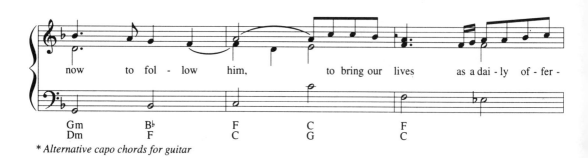

* *Alternative capo chords for guitar*

Copyright © 1983 Kingsway's Thankyou Music, P.O. Box 75,
Eastbourne, East Sussex BN23 6NW. Used by permission.

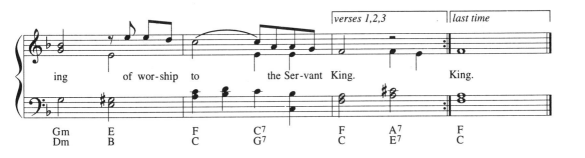

ing   of wor-ship to   the Ser-vant King.   King.

Gm   E   F   C⁷   F   A⁷   F
Dm   B   C   G⁷   C   E⁷   C

2. There in the garden of tears,
    my heavy load he chose to bear;
    his heart with sorrow was torn,
    'Yet not my will but yours', he said.

3. Come, see his hands and his feet,
    and scars that speak of sacrifice,
    hands that flung stars into space
    to cruel nails surrendered.

4. So let us learn how to serve,
    and in our lives enthrone him;
    each other's needs to prefer,
    for it is Christ we're serving.

Words and music: Graham Kendrick

HOSANNA

Lively

1. Ho - san - na, ho - san - na, ho-san-na in the high - est! Ho-
san - na, ho - san - na, ho-san-na in the high - est!
Lord, we lift up your name, with hearts full of praise;
be ex - alt - ed, O Lord, my God! Ho-san-na in the high - est!

2. Glory, glory, glory to the King of kings!
Glory, glory, glory to the King of kings!
Lord, we lift up your name,
with hearts full of praise;
be exalted, O Lord, my God!
Glory to the King of kings!

Words and music: Carl Tuttle

Copyright © 1985 Mercy/Vineyard Publishing. Administered in the UK and Eire by Integrity's Hosanna! Music,
P.O. Box 101, Eastbourne, East Sussex BN21 4SZ. International copyright secured. Used by permission.

AS THE DEER

2. I want you more than gold or silver,
   only you can satisfy.
   You alone are the real joy-giver
   and the apple of my eye.

3. You're my friend and you're my brother,
   even though you are a king.
   I love you more than any other,
   so much more than anything.

Words and music: Martin Nystrom

Copyright © 1983 Restoration Music Ltd. Administered by Sovereign Music U.K.,
P.O. Box 356, Leighton Buzzard, Beds LU7 8WP. Used by permission.

JESUS SHALL TAKE THE HIGHEST HONOUR

Copyright © 1988 Sovereign Lifestyle Music, P.O. Box 356, Leighton Buzzard, Beds. LU7 8WP.
Used by permission.

Words and music: Chris Bowater

GREAT IS THE LORD

Worshipfully

Great is the Lord and most wor-thy of praise, the
A D A

ci-ty of our God, the ho-ly place, the joy of the whole earth.
D F#m(A) A

Great is the
Bm(D) E A

Lord in whom we have the vic-to-ry, He aids us a-gainst the e-ne-
D A D

my, we bow down on our knees. And
F#m(A) A Bm(D) E

Copyright © 1985 Body Songs. Administered by CopyCare Ltd, P.O. Box 77,
Hailsham, East Sussex BN27 3EF. Used by permission.

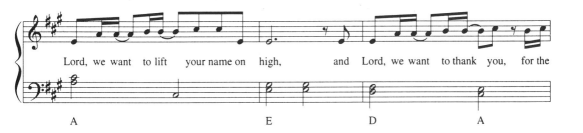

Lord, we want to lift your name on high, and Lord, we want to thank you, for the

A   E   D   A

works we've done in our lives; and Lord, we trust in your un-fail-ing love, for

Bm(D)   D   A   E

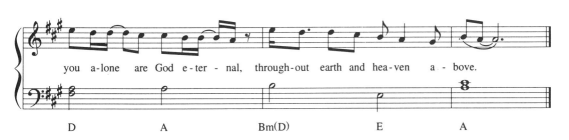

you a-lone are God e-ter-nal, through-out earth and hea-ven a-bove.

D   A   Bm(D)   E   A

Words and music: Steve McEwan

FATHER GOD I WONDER

I will sing your praises

Words and music: Ian Smale

Copyright © 1984 Kingsway's Thankyou Music, P.O. Box 75,
Eastbourne, East Sussex BN23 6NW. Used by permission.

BE STILL, FOR THE PRESENCE OF THE LORD

Reverently

1. Be still, for the pre-sence of the Lord, the Ho-ly One, is here;
come bow be-fore him now with re-ve-rence and fear;
in him no sin is found – we stand on ho-ly ground.
Be still, for the pre-sence of the Lord, the Ho-ly One, is here.

2. Be still, for the glory of the Lord is shining all around;
   he burns with holy fire, with splendour he is crowned.
   How awesome is the sight, our radiant king of light!
   Be still, for the glory of the Lord is shining all around.

3. Be still, for the power of the Lord is moving in this place,
   he comes to cleanse and heal, to minister his grace.
   No work too hard for him, in faith receive from him;
   be still, for the power of the Lord is moving in this place.

Words and music: David J Evans

Copyright © 1986 Kingsway's Thankyou Music, P.O. Box 75,
Eastbourne, East Sussex BN23 6NW. Used by permission.

I AM A NEW CREATION

Copyright © 1983 Kingsway's Thankyou Music, P.O. Box 75,
Eastbourne, East Sussex BN23 6NW. Used by permission.

and I will sing of all that you have done.

C   Am   F   G

A joy that knows no li - mit. a light - ness in

C   G   C

my spi - rit, here in the grace of God I stand.

F   C   F   G   C   F   C

Words and music: Dave Bilbrough

MAJESTY

© Copyright 1976 Rocksmith Music. Administered by Leosong Copyright Service Ltd,
Greenland Place, 115-123 Bayham Street, Camden Town, London NW1 0AG. Used by permission.

fy, come glo-ri-fy Christ Je-sus the King.

Ma - jes-ty, wor-ship his ma - jes-ty, Je-sus who

died, now glo-ri-fied, King of all kings.

Words and music: Jack W Hayford

GIVE THANKS WITH A GRATEFUL HEART

Copyright © 1978 Integrity's Hosanna! Music/administered by Kingsway's Thankyou Music, P.O. Box 75, Eastbourne, East Sussex BN23 6NW. Used by permission.

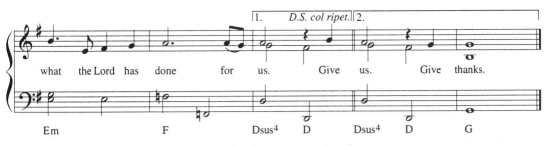

Words and music: Henry Smith

SUCH LOVE

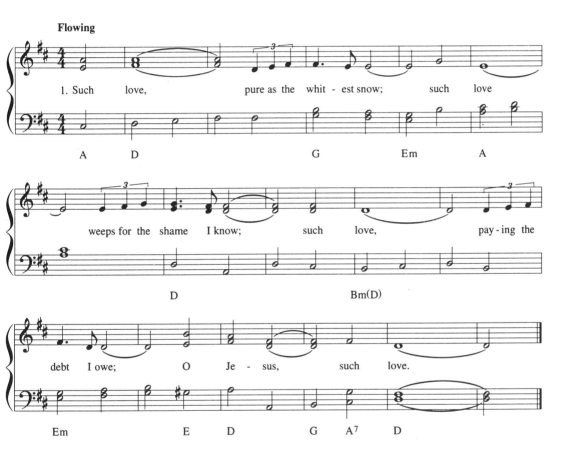

2. Such love, stilling my restlessness;
   such love, filling my emptiness;
   such love, showing me holiness;
   O Jesus, such love.

3. Such love springs from eternity;
   such love, streaming through history;
   such love, fountain of life to me;
   O Jesus, such love.

Words and music: Graham Kendrick

Copyright © 1988 Make Way Music, P.O. Box 263, Croydon, Surrey CR9 5AP.
International copyright secured. All rights reserved. Used by permission.

COME ON AND CELEBRATE

Words and music: Dave Bankhead and Patricia Morgan

Copyright © 1984 Kingway's Thankyou Music, P.O. Box 75, Eastbourne, East Sussex BN23 6NW. Used by permission.

ALL HEAVEN DECLARES

Majestically

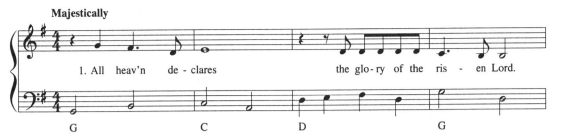

1. All heav'n de-clares the glo-ry of the ris - en Lord.

Who can com - pare with the beau-ty of the Lord?

For - e-ver he will be the Lamb u-pon the throne.

I glad-ly bow the knee and wor-ship him a - lone.

2. I will proclaim
   the glory of the risen Lord.
   Who once was slain
   to reconcile man to God.
   Forever you will be
   the Lamb upon the throne.
   I gladly bow the knee
   and worship you alone.

Words and music: Noel and Tricia Richards

© Copyright 1987 Kingsway's Thankyou Music, P.O. Box 75,
Eastbourne, East Sussex BN23 6NW. Used by permission.

JESUS, WE CELEBRATE YOUR VICTORY

Copyright © 1987 Kingsway's Thankyou Music, P.O Box 75,
Eastbourne, East Sussex BN23 6NW. Used by permission.

long - er to be sub - ject to a yoke of sla - ve - ry;

so we're re - joic - ing in God's vic - to - ry, our

hearts re - spond - ing to his love.

2. His Spirit in us releases us from fear,
   the way to him is open, with boldness we draw near.
   And in his presence our problems disappear;
   our hearts responding to his love.

Words and music: John Gibson

LORD, THE LIGHT OF YOUR LOVE

Shine, Jesus, Shine

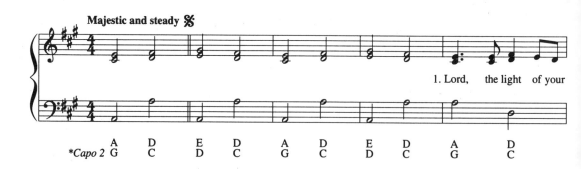

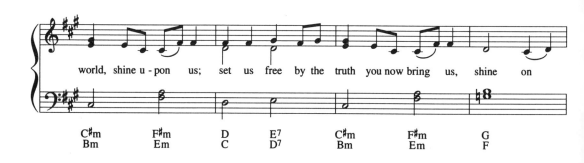

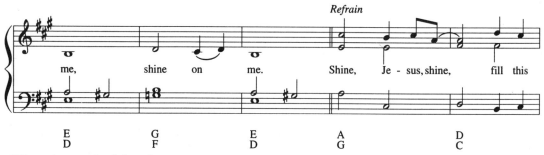

*Alternative capo chords for guitar

Copyright © 1987 Make Way Music, P.O. Box 263, Croydon, Surrey CR9 5AP.
International copyright secured. All rights reserved. Used by permission.

land with the Fa-ther's glo-ry; blaze, Spi-rit, blaze, set our hearts on

Bm E E⁷ A D Bm
Am D D⁷ G C Am

fire. Flow, ri-ver, flow, flood the na - tions with grace and mer-cy;

G E A D Bm E E⁷
F D G C Am D D⁷

D.S. | last time

send forth your word, Lord, and let there be light!

A D Bm E⁷ A D A
G C Am D⁷ G C G

2. Lord, I come to your awesome presence.
   from the shadows into your radiance;
   by the blood I may enter your brightness,
   search me, try me, consume all my darkness,
   shine on me, shine on me.

3. As we gaze on your kingly brightness
   so our faces display your likeness,
   ever changing from glory to glory,
   mirrored here may our lives tell your story,
   shine on me, shine on me.

Words and music: Graham Kendrick